## Ad
## News fro

*"Carolyn Redman writes hard, clear and lovingly about her experience with breast cancer. Her insight, wisdom and humor can guide each of us on this path whether we be supporting a woman with breast cancer or experiencing it ourselves. Don't miss this read, and then pass it forward gratefully."*

—Kathryn Klein Havens, MD, Director of Women's Health, Zablocki VA Medical Center and former Board member of ABCD (After Breast Cancer Diagnosis)

*"Redman's words are both honest and touching, and this is indeed sacred ground we have been invited to walk on in News from Lake Boobbegone. The personal struggles and triumphs shared make opening this book nothing short of an honor."*

—Aaron Jonasen, MS, Professional Counselor, Stillwaters Cancer Support Center

*"As a cancer survivor myself, I found myself completely immersed in this very poignant memoir from beginning to end. Ms. Redman shared her story so honestly and with such vulnerability; by the end I felt transported into her personal "Oz". I would recommend News from Lake Boobbegone to anyone looking to gain insight into the cancer 'trip'."*

—Maria Voermans, Wellness Coordinator, Small Stones Wellness Center

*"As a fellow breast cancer survivor, I was often left wanting as I read others "memoirs" in search of the right approach to get me through treatment. Reading Carolyn Redman's account was not only a wonderfully easy read, but, for me, hit on the right combination of emotions (anger, fear, hope and, of course gratitude) while providing strategies for not just surviving but growing through the process. Its humanity and vulnerability make it easy to reflect on your own challenges and know that you can make it!"*

—Karen Marcdante, Physician and fellow inhabitant of Lake Boobbegone

*"A heart-felt, touching account of the author's journey through breast cancer. Her dry sense of humor and eloquent turn of phrase are highly engaging. Ms. Redman has created a very accessible story likely to provide comfort and support to those following in her footsteps."*

—Bonnie Nussbaum, Holistic Coach and Psychologist

*"As a medical provider reading News from Lake Boobbegone, I am reminded again how essential it is that we treat each person with mindful compassion. Our words, looks, touches and attention reaches the soul of the patient we are trying to heal. We should choose these carefully. I applaud Carolyn Redman's honesty, humor and willingness to put all her fears out there as she takes us through her story. I would recommend, not only for people going through cancer treatment, but also for all of us in the medical/caregiving field. It reminds us why we are here."*

—Diane Keller, Occupational therapist, Clinical Cancer Center

*"Being diagnosed with cancer can feel like being transported to another world, and when Carolyn Redman finds herself in this strange land, she forges ahead with brains, heart and courage. News from Lake Boobbegone is her collection of field notes from the journey, and with honesty and humor she shares the bits and pieces of wisdom she's uncovered along the way. As a breast cancer survivor, finding myself and my own story within the pages of Lake Boobbegone is a testament to the sisterhood of survivorship, and to the power of leaning on and learning from one another. Redman's strength is an inspiration, and her story is a gift."*

—Marloe Esch, BSN, RN, OCN

*"As a hairstylist for 40 years counseling women through their fears of losing their personal beauty with the absence of their hair and eyebrows, I would recommend News from Lake Boobbegone to ease their worries. Carolyn Redman explains her feelings on how she created her new image and how friends, family and professionals helped her regain herself. This book is critically helpful for women navigating the complicated world of breast cancer procedures. It is written in an intimate style with humor, unrelenting honesty and courage."*

—Sharon Gamm, Hairstylist and volunteer,
American Cancer Society—Look Good Feel Better program

*"Carolyn Redman's wit, candor and clever analogies ease your walk with her through the dreaded Land of Cancer. Her insights into healing mind and spirit as well as body can inspire those who find themselves in this strange place where suddenly everything is as it never was. I will be adding News from Lake Boobbegone to the list of recommended readings for those I work with who are making this journey into the Land of Cancer."*

—Rose Koremenos, RN, BSN, Holistic Practitioner

# News from Lake Boobbegone

## A Breast Cancer Memoir from the Heart

**Carolyn Redman**

Green Bay, WI 54311

This book is a true story about the real life of Carolyn Redman of Milwaukee, Wisconsin. All names and locations are real. Permission has been obtained where possible for the use of names in the book, and changed, where persons wanted their identity to remain anonymous. This book reflects the opinions of the author and her life's decisions. Written Dreams Publishing does not approve, condone or disapprove of these opinions.



Editor: Brittiany Koren
Copy-editor: Jessie Harrison
Cover art design: Barbra Sprangers
Interior layout: Ed Vincent of ENC Graphic Services
Category: Nonfiction/Women's Health Memoir
Description: *Insightful and uplifting,* ***News from Lake Boobbegone*** *is a memoir written by Wisconsin author, Carolyn Redman, regarding her decisions and treatments of breast cancer.*
Paperback ISBN: 978-0-9987623-6-4
Ebook ISBN: 978-0-9987623-7-1
Library of Congress Catalog Data: Applied for.

First Edition published by Written Dreams Publishing in April, 2017.

WD
PUBLISHING
Green Bay, WI 54311

*For the recently diagnosed.*

*And for Tom, who never once left my side.*

# Preface

News *from Lake Boobbegone* started out as informative emails to family and friends in an attempt to limit phone calls and keep from having to tell the same story over and over while keeping them apprised of my medical condition. What it morphed into is an honest account of my experience with breast cancer that, in the end, helped me heal.

Throughout my treatment, I was encouraged to formally compile these updates with the goal of publishing them. Since this encouragement came from my faithful readers, who know me and have a genuine interest in my well-being, I assumed that was where the interest in or value of my story ended. Before seriously considering this project, I asked myself a critical question: *Does the world really need another breast cancer memoir?*

My initial response was probably not. But then, after going through treatment, I realized that no two women experience or react to the illness or the treatment exactly the same way. This is the case even if they have the same diagnosis, team of doctors, and treatment plan. From that point on, I was able to see the value of my individual experience and how it might help others, which is my sole desire and intent.

Writing has always helped me make sense of things, but I never realized the power it has to heal. The updates themselves are without a doubt the most stream-of-consciousness writing that I have ever done, straight from my heart, and with very little editing—only enough to add clarity.

The short essays between numbered entries are my attempt to fill in the informational and emotional gaps. I've had time to step back and process everything my body, mind, and spirit have experienced since the day I was initially diagnosed. It's true what they say about hindsight.

The title is an obvious and deliberate homage to Garrison Keillor, who, through his weekly broadcast of *A Prairie Home Companion,* taught me the value of a good story, even if you're from the Midwest. I intend to keep writing, keep healing, and more than anything, keep hoping that by telling my story I will help someone else in some small way.

So here's what happened to me and how I ended up at Lake Boobbegone.

Carolyn Redman
April 2017

## My First Cancer Poem

On Tuesday,
a routine mammogram
exposes suspicious white dots
clustered like honey bees.
Only biopsied bees reveal their intent,
with pretty pink ribbons as your reward.
Tag. You're it.

# The Diagnosis

*"Cancer Is a Word, Not a Sentence."*
—Robert Buckman, MD

Without fail and without your permission, a cancer diagnosis transports you into unfamiliar territory physically, mentally, emotionally, and spiritually. When my surgeon started saying the words invasive lobular carcinoma, mastectomy, lymph node involvement, chemotherapy, and radiation therapy, and topped it off with survival statistics, I felt just like Dorothy in *The Wizard of Oz*. There she was, minding her own business on a dreary Midwest farm and before she had time to take a deep breath, she was spinning around inside a cyclone. After I'd seen the imaging of my left breast and the way in which the cancer chose to spread like gossamer, I knew it had to come off. Saying that out loud for the first time immediately swept me into the eye wall of the cyclone.

Fortunately, my husband, Tom was with me, because I literally could not comprehend anything the surgeon said after that. With a mastectomy abruptly added to my "to do" list, we were ushered from a brightly lit exam room into a dimly lit conference room where a nurse-navigator came in to get me up and running on the data-driven cancer conveyor belt. With a few gentle keystrokes, she silently sounded the alarm letting everyone know that the cancer center had a reluctant new member. She handed me a large white binder with the cancer center logo on it. The binder contained an extraordinary amount of information on what to expect in the coming months and who to expect it from. *Really? There are handouts for breast cancer?*

The binder was only the beginning. Three quarters of the way through her obviously well-worn presentation, I burst into all-consuming, can't-catch-your-breath, people-feel-incredibly-awkward-around-you tears. I didn't break down in front of the surgeon out of what I deemed a courtesy; as a rule, they don't have time for their own tears, let alone yours.

Handing me a box of cheap, scratchy hospital tissues, the nurse said, "Oh, weren't you expecting this?"

Tom immediately came to my rescue and said exactly what I was thinking but couldn't verbalize between sobs, "Who the hell expects this?"

A seemingly endless, awkward silence ensued while I tried desperately to pull it together. Ordinarily, Tom would have comforted me without hesitation, but I had given him specific instructions on the drive in not to touch me, pat my leg, hold my hand, or give me sympathetic looks during the appointment. I knew if he did any of those things, I would only start crying or cry even harder, which at that point I couldn't imagine was possible.

The nurse gave Tom a sideways, judgmental "why aren't you consoling your wife?" look, forcing him to come to his own defense and tell her that he was just following orders.

More parting gifts ensued, consisting of a hospital tote

bag to carry my cumbersome cancer center binder along with a heart-shaped fabric pillow engineered by sympathetic church-lady volunteers to tuck under my arm after my left breast went to live with Jesus. I rolled my salty, red-rimmed eyes at what, in that moment, I considered an insignificant, parochial gesture and stuffed the pillow in my new tote bag so we could get the hell out of there.

As it turned out, that lime green paisley print pillow gave me more comfort in the coming months than I could have ever imagined. It was extremely practical, fit perfectly under my arm, and gently cushioned my incisions, which allowed me to sleep. It helped me transition from having a body part to not having it. People I didn't even know, and who may have been through some variation of this nightmare themselves, wanted to help me. This was a time for gratitude and not my signature eye roll, but it was way too early in the game for that realization. I wouldn't appreciate this anonymous act of kindness until after my surgery. (I still sleep with that pillow tucked under my arm on occasion, even though my physical wounds have long since healed.)

As soon as we left the nurse-navigator, my cell phone rang with other cancer center team members who were trying to do their jobs. For starters, I had to pick a date for the surgery and schedule a myriad of preoperative diagnostic tests.

When the first call came in, I was standing in a stall in the cancer center bathroom, still trying to compose myself and stop the bout of post-crying hiccups. I had the sense not to answer the phone at that point, but later I counted three messages from three different clinics on my home phone. It was all happening way too fast. Clearly, I was up inside the cyclone without a paddle.

# Christmas, 2013

*"It's the Most Wonderful Time of the Year."*
—Andy Williams

My diagnosis came right before Christmas, which seemed to make it even worse. I got some things that weren't on my Christmas list: a CT scan, a bone scan, a sentinel node biopsy, a plastic surgery consult, and the only thing I really wanted—a second opinion.

Since I had some sort of medical appointment every other day, having cancer quickly became my fulltime job.

*Relieved* isn't a strong enough word to describe my reaction when my CT and bone scans came back negative. Waiting for those results was grueling. I had learned that the sentinel node is the first lymph node to which the cancer cells are most likely to spread; that's what a biopsy determines.

The day before surgery, a tracer material is injected into the breast in an effort to help the surgeon locate the sentinel nodes during surgery. You read that correctly, *injected into the breast*. The patient, in this case—me—is supine on an exam table for however long it takes the tracer material to find the sentinel node. My experience took a little over two hours. That didn't surprise me because I was always the kid in school who handed her test in last in hopes that time alone would ensure a better grade.

The radiologist prefaced the procedure by telling me that some women claimed what was about to happen to me was the worst pain they had ever felt in their entire lives. *What? Why was she saying this out loud to me?* I understand the need to prepare a patient for possible discomfort, but the *worst pain ever*? Surely, the worst pain ever was yet to come and reserved for the mastectomy itself. Clearly, she had flunked bedside manner in medical school.

The radiology technician who had prepped me for the procedure looked horrified at the doctor's explanation and compassionately chimed in that she had heard other women describe the procedure as an extended bee sting.

*Oh, okay, that I could handle.* Biopsies are not fun, but they are capable of unearthing an awful lot of diagnostic information that can help the doctor determine the stage of the cancer, along with a customized treatment plan. Anyway, that's how they sell it.

Once I was prepped, injected, and draped, they let my friend, Beth come into the room to keep me company until the tracer material made its way to the sentinel node. This would be the first of many times Beth sat by my side, doing her best to distract me during an uncomfortable medical procedure. She arrived with a stack of magazines and proceeded to read the latest Hollywood gossip aloud. No matter how old you are, there is something nostalgic and soothing about someone reading aloud to you—even if it's about the inane exploits of celebrities.

There were no decorations, presents, or family gatherings that Christmas. Tom and I circled the wagons knowing full well that things were going to get a lot worse before they got better. And they did indeed.

# Impossible Choices

*"A huge part of being a feminist is giving other women*
*the freedom to make choices*
*you might not necessarily make yourself."*
—Lena Dunham

When cancer is detected in one breast, one of the treatment options is to have both breasts removed, even though the statistical likelihood of the cancer spreading to the unaffected breast is extremely low. I guess you could call it the "better-safe-than-sorry" approach.

After hearing and researching the statistics and learning about the way breast cancer tends to behave, it made absolutely no sense *for me* to have a double mastectomy, especially since there was no detectable disease in my right breast. Getting a second opinion was paramount in helping me understand the situation and make one of the most difficult decisions of my life. Believe me, the last thing I wanted was another medical appointment, but I couldn't go into this without finding another breast surgeon from a different institution to weigh in on my predicament.

It's always been my tendency to shop around for car insurance or get more than one quote from different contractors on a new roof, so why wouldn't I take the time to ensure I was making the most informed decision possible, especially when body parts were at stake? Not all insurance companies see it that way, of course. They expect patients to find peace of mind on their own dime. This wasn't the time to be cheap; the second opinion and I were worth every penny.

When I asked my original surgeon what he thought I should do, his insightful but rather cryptic response was: "It depends on what kind of woman you are." He had given me all of the data, and I had talked this over ad nauseam with every reasonably intelligent person I knew. Clearly, there was no statistical reason for me to have a double mastectomy, unless I was going to react to this disease by living in a constant state of anxiety, always wondering if the cancer *had spread or was going to spread* to my other breast. If that fear was going to trump the quality of my life, it might make sense to choose a double mastectomy. That's where push came to shove, and I had to do some serious soul searching before making my decision. To his credit and without judgment, the surgeon was willing to do what made me feel the most comfortable.

My second surgical opinion concurred with the first; my left breast had to go. The more limited surgeries—basic lumpectomies—are common now, but I had already exhausted that treatment option in 2009 when I was diagnosed with lobular carcinoma *in situ* that after a biopsy was staged at zero. All that really meant (I'm over simplifying here) was that I had some scary looking cells, which as far as the pathologist could tell, were encapsulated and staying put.

I had a lumpectomy to remove the suspicious looking cells with no adjuvant therapy since the "cancer" was staged at zero, which to this day doesn't make a whole lot of sense to me. In my mind, you either have cancer or you don't. (Believe it or not, "stage zero" remains up for debate in the medical community.)

Anyway, fast-forward to my 2014 mammogram to when I'm supposed to get the ever popular five-year all clear, but the cells are no longer encapsulated, have run amok, and invaded my entire breast. Since it was lobular and spread out like a spider web, I had no lump, pain, or obvious physical signs. My mammograms since the lumpectomy had all been clear. Imagine my surprise when I was diagnosed and told differently.

I had an odd sense of relief knowing that the second surgical opinion had, without a doubt, concurred with the first. The option of a contralateral prophylactic mastectomy (removal of the healthy breast) was still on the table and a decision only I could make. This was one time in my life I wouldn't have minded someone telling me exactly what to do, even Tom, especially Tom. But we both knew the stakes were too high; only I could make this decision, and all he could do was support whatever choice I made, which is exactly what he did. Despite the number of women diagnosed with breast cancer and all of the support out there, when push comes to shove, these are incredibly personal and solitary decisions.

Without trying to sound glib, the removal of a healthy breast along with its cancerous counterpart in hopes of preventing a recurrence almost seemed *trendy* to me. Around that time, certain Hollywood celebrities had gone public with their personal decisions about preventing cancer or the recurrence of cancer. For some of these well-known women, the decision was based on genetic testing. However, I had waited weeks for the results of genetic testing, which came back inconclusive. Both surgeons advised against making surgical decisions based on those results. The tests revealed that I didn't have the hereditary breast cancer BRCA gene, which would have made the decision of having a double mastectomy easier for me, as it had done so for many women.

Plenty of people weighed in on what they thought I should do. The ones who voted for the double mastectomy were partly motivated by fear but also, I like to think, a sincere desire for my well-being. I explained the statistics the best I could and how it felt to me, that removing the other perfectly fine breast would be like chopping off one of my hands, and most of them understood or at least tried to.

Both surgeons thought I was making a rational decision based on the diagnostic evidence and statistical data. Removing only the cancerous breast meant less surgery, less anesthesia, less time in the operating room, less chance of an infection, and a quicker recovery time, which all made perfect sense to me. As my second opinion surgeon observed, "sometimes it takes more courage *not* to have surgery." Whether or not that's true, it was important for me to realize that like everything else in life, and as impossible as it seemed, *I had a choice*.

# Plastic Surgery Consult

(The day after Christmas)

*"A Good Man is Hard to Find."*
—Flannery O'Conner

A crack-of-dawn office visit with a plastic surgeon was the first sub-specialist appointment on my cancer itinerary. Tom and I were still reeling from the diagnosis, so Christmas had come and gone without the usual fanfare.

An early appointment boded well with my "let's get this over with and go out for breakfast" personality type. Once in the exam room, I was handed another hefty binder filled with information on everything you always wanted to know about breast reconstructive surgery. Apparently, no Cliff Notes exist for anything cancer-related. Great, I thought, more homework with impossible decisions ahead.

I made it clear to the nurse that this appointment was for the purpose of gathering information only. I wasn't about to sign up for any one of the many plans they had to offer. For all of the attention breasts get in our society, they suddenly become incredibly expendable when the word cancer is involved. My surgery was scheduled for February 4th, so I had plenty of time to research options and figure out what to do. I hadn't made the final decision about a double mastectomy, so that elephant was still in the room. Plenty of women opt for no reconstruction at all, which is an extremely brave choice in my opinion.

To be honest, I didn't think all that much about my breasts until I was about to lose one. I was still having trouble believing that any of this was real, and that in a few short weeks, a part of my body was going to be surgically removed.

In general, women have two reconstructive options: silicone gel implants or a tissue transfer that would take fat from my abdomen to rebuild a new breast. Both options seemed a little on the Frankenstein side to me. The surgeon assured me that implants had come a long way and that they were perfectly safe, but I remained skeptical, as is my nature. How could anything implanted in you be perfectly safe? I must admit, the tissue transfer was tempting at first because it seemed as if I could get a tummy tuck thrown in for free. But it also meant major abdominal surgery on top of everything else. I had chemotherapy and radiation treatments on the horizon. How much could I ask of my poor unsuspecting body? And in the grand scheme of things, how important was it that I have cleavage?

The surgeon handed me yet another binder full of before and after photos of what he deemed successful breast reconstructions. I don't know about Tom, but looking at these headless glamour shots made me more than a little uncomfortable and somehow seemed inappropriate, but how else to sell his work other than through a portfolio? Surgeons are anatomical mechanics; they remove parts, replace parts, and keep things running against all odds. A guy I had met a mere 20 minutes ago was going to change the structure of my physical body as if he were changing a tire. Granted, he wasn't quite that cavalier about it. He sincerely acknowledged the emotional toll of such a procedure, but this was clearly all in a day's work for him. The waiting room chock-full of anxious patients in varying stages of disrepair confirmed my impressions.

Tom and I left the surgeon's office with more questions than answers that day. I planned to call a few friends who had been in similar circumstances and ask what route they had taken and why. I had what seemed like plenty of time. We stopped for breakfast in a feeble attempt at normalcy. As usual, I couldn't decide what to order, so how the hell was I ever going to make these surgical decisions? I was in deep.

Tom and I sipped our coffee and studied the menu in silence. Suddenly, and with complete sincerity, he looked straight at me and said: "You know I don't care if you have boobs or not, right? Nothing can change how much I love you."

The ability to blink back tears in public was something I was seriously considering adding to my résumé. Tom definitely knew how and when to cut to the chase. And then I realized how spot on Flannery O'Conner really was.

The waitress showed up to take our order at the most inopportune moment. Eyes brimming with tears, I ordered the veggie omelet with a side of fruit. I took a deep breath and realized that was the only decision I needed to make today.

## Ode to the Recently Diagnosed

Cells gather in silence without any pain,
Such a choreographed cancerous plot;
Our milky breasts the prize to gain
Be stoic, you women, endure your lot,
Betrayed by your own anatomy.
These images mimic a bright constellation
Randomly trumping our lives
How much will there remain of me?
As the surgeon begins without hesitation,
The moment of truth has arrived.

# The Actual Surgery

Commonly referred to as *The Day the Earth Stood Still.*

*"Let everything happen to you: beauty and the terror. Just keep going. No feeling is final."*
—Rainer Maria Rilke

Prior to my mastectomy, I'd had only two surgical experiences on my résumé: a tonsillectomy way back in 1968 and a lumpectomy in 2009—and, to be honest, both experiences left me with indelible physical and emotional scars. My left mastectomy was scheduled on a bitterly cold morning in February. Tom and I made the 4:30 a.m. drive to the hospital in darkness and silence. We held hands and had the sense of being the only two people left on Earth. That lasted until we arrived at the hospital that was teeming with life and all lit up like a space station.

The first thing we encountered was a line of other people checking in for surgery. It looked like a deli. I was stunned by the numbers and couldn't help but wonder what was wrong with all of these people. Everyone looked fine, including me—especially me. Maybe this was a big mistake after all.

I didn't have to wait long before the surgical staff was

ready for me and the seemingly endless preoperative procedures got underway. For at least two hours, the questions and consent forms kept coming at me. The surgeon and the anesthesiologist stopped by, along with a smattering of residents, nurses, technicians, and to top it all off, the hospital chaplain. That one threw me a little. I think it was the first time I thought this might not turn out well.

Tom was with me for this part of the pre-op but the time came when he had to leave, and I was taken further into the bowels of the surgical suite for even more preparation. He kissed me gently on my forehead and said he'd be there when I woke up. I couldn't look directly at him or I would have started to cry. I had made it this far into pre-op without shedding a single tear and was bound and determined to keep a stiff upper lip.

And I did, at least until the very last nurse came in to see me before I was wheeled into the operating room. I'd been poked, prodded, and questioned all morning and was now connected to beeping machines with more wires than the Flying Wallendas used during their entire career. Clearly, there was no escape. I was lying flat on my back with my blue surgical cap on, which meant it was show time.

That's when Becky came in. She looked like the rest of the staff in her surgical scrubs and the same blue bonnet I'd been issued. She introduced herself and put her hand on mine for no other reason than to comfort me. She looked directly at me with the softest sincerity and said others would come and go, but she would stay in the operating room with me the entire time. Despite all of my efforts to thwart them, the tears finally broke through and streamed down the side of my face.

Becky was prepared. Tissue in hand, she caught my tears

before they had a chance to land and pool in my ears. And then she said four simple words with confidence and resolve: *"You can do this."*

There is no greater act of surrender than being anesthetized. Thankfully, it doesn't take long. I have no doubt that the next four hours were harder on Tom than on me. After all, I got to sleep through surgery; he had to wait, and wait, and wait some more. Anyone who knows Tom is aware that waiting around is not one of his strong suits. But there he was, as promised, sitting next to my bed when I woke up looking worse than I felt.

The anesthesiologist and pain management team did an incredible job because I was in no physical pain. I was scheduled to stay in the hospital for two nights. With the exception of going home to shower and feed the cat, Tom stayed with me the entire time.

I had come prepared and quickly set up a pop-up healing altar with a beautiful rose quartz angel my Reiki practitioner had given me, a small image of White Tara (a female Buddhist deity that brings compassion, longevity, healing, and serenity), and some essential oils in an attempt to eliminate that all-encompassing antiseptic hospital smell.

The nurses and aides were amazing. Tess quickly became my favorite. She was young and upbeat without being obnoxious. There's nice and then there's too nice; it's a fine line with me—and I know others have the same boundaries. Propping people up with pillows was her specialty, and she wouldn't give up until I was completely comfortable and able to sleep.

I had to faint before my surgeon would come to see me in the hospital. The residents usually handle all of the follow-up unless there's a problem. Apparently fainting is a problem. In order to have my incredibly intrusive urinary catheter removed, I had to prove that I could sit up, stand up, and use the bathroom on my own. Really? That's it? What are we waiting for?

I had been lying flat on my back for over 24 hours, hadn't had anything to eat, and was on some very serious pain medication, so when I stood up for the first time, my body decided against it. My eyes rolled back in my head and down I went. Luckily, I was right next to the bed flanked by Tom and a nurse and came in for a soft landing.

After my fainting spell I was tucked back into bed, and my surgeon broke the news that he wanted to go back in for more lymph nodes in the next two to three weeks. The surgical residents alluded to this possibility, but I had just filed that under the "there's been some misunderstanding" column in my head.

This was disheartening news to say the least. I was supposed to be done with the surgery part of this ordeal. I was going home tomorrow and didn't want to come back, ever.

But in the end I did, and the surgeon took 12 more lymph nodes for his collection.

# News from Lake Boobbegone

## Part 1

### February 11, 2014

*"Home is the nicest word there is."*
—Laura Ingalls Wilder

I went home on Friday. The surgery took longer than expected. My left breast is gone, although where exactly it went I'm not yet sure, along with three lymph nodes. The surgeon may have to go back in for more. I wasn't expecting to hear that news, but I'll know more next week Thursday when I see him again. Fortunately, I have almost no physical pain.

I can't say enough about the competency and kindness of the hospital staff—truly an amazing team of professionals.

I had a plastic surgery follow-up yesterday. Everyone says I "look great," but I think that's relative. They removed one drain from my side and will take the other one out on Thursday, and then physical therapy starts on Friday. I see the medical oncologist in a few days, so we'll see what he recommends.

Tom has been wonderful. He stayed with me both nights in the hospital and has been taking great care of me at home. I am so grateful for the support and love surrounding me. I have my weepy moments and am having trouble looking at myself right now. I never had the greatest body image, but this is really, really hard.

Ever forward.

# News from Lake Boobbegone

## Part 2

### February 15, 2014

(Ten days post-op)

*"Courage is grace under pressure."*
—Ernest Hemingway

I started physical therapy yesterday and now have a new angel/physical therapist in my life. It feels good to know how to safely and slowly start moving my left arm again. At this point in time, I'm weak as a kitten and can't even open the refrigerator door without wincing in pain. Regaining mobility and range of motion is going to take patience, time, and effort.

After therapy, I saw my surgeon to go over the pathology report. The news wasn't what I wanted to hear. The cancer in my left breast was more extensive than the imaging tests detected and has now been upgraded from *Stage I* to *Stage IIIa*. I was told there are only four stages of cancer, so scoring higher was not a good thing in my case. Upgrades usually come with a bottle of champagne; there was none in sight.

The surgeon removed three lymph nodes; the first two were positive and the third had isolated tumor cells. Bottom line, he wants to go back in and take more nodes, as my lymphatic system appears to be losing at Pac-Man. He had warned me of this possibility, which has now become a reality. He didn't take more originally because the nodes were so small. He himself seemed surprised that they tested positive.

As much as I didn't want more surgery, I appreciated the surgeon's less aggressive approach at the start. I think it was a really tough call for him.

So, we'll schedule the additional procedure in the next two to three weeks, giving my body a chance to heal as much as it can from the mastectomy. Apparently, this new surgery will not interfere with the reconstructive surgery or physical therapy.

Because of the cancer upgrade, radiation therapy was added to my treatment plan. So in addition to meeting with my medical oncologist to plot a chemo course, I need to shop around for a radiation oncologist.

I plan to get through this with as much grace as I can possibly muster and remain grateful along the way for all of the people who are helping me physically, biochemically, mentally, emotionally, and spiritually. Time alone will tell.

# News from Lake Boobbegone

## Part 3

### February 21, 2014

*"We're all just walking each other home."*
—Ram Dass

Anyone who knows me, even remotely, is aware that I love the film *The Wizard of Oz* and will watch it several times throughout the year. And anyone who knows me, even remotely, is also aware that I can't pass up a good metaphor, especially a cinematic one. It's the English major/movie lover in me. So here goes.

I have been spending an inordinate amount of time at the cancer center (aka the Haunted Forest), visiting their specialty clinics, lying in enormous scanning machines, holding my breath when instructed, and answering the same questions over and over. At home, I spend hours searching online for cancer treatment options.

While still on medical leave from the mastectomy and with some time to kill between appointments the other day,

I decided to pop into the office to say hello to my coworkers (the Munchkins). They all gathered around my cube, some venturing down from Emerald City (the 7th floor) just to see me. Hugs all around, sincere well wishes, compliments, presents, all the while secretly hoping that I would come back soon so they could stop having to do my work. I have worked with some of these people for nearly twenty years and am amazed at how much you can care about people who drive you crazy on a daily basis. Sounds like a family to me.

In walks Bob, my boss, aptly cast as the Scarecrow. He and I have been on the road together a long time. He is wiser than he ever lets on, always points me in the right direction, and most importantly, he has the patience to let me come to my own conclusions no matter how long it takes. Working for a pediatrician has its advantages, especially when you've still got some growing up of your own to do. I can see why Dorothy missed the Scarecrow most of all when she had to return home; the same holds true for me.

The Cowardly Lion in this analogy, although far from cowardly, is my husband, Tom. He appears gruff and is always ready to go to battle for me anytime, anywhere. This is exactly the kind of person you want on your side when you are navigating Cancerland. Without question, he bivouacked with me while I was in the hospital and plans to again for my second surgery, which is scheduled for February 28th.

Tom has lived with me for twenty-three years, which takes a lot of courage, even on a good day. He's turned out to be quite the medic, draining things and bandaging things, all without complaining or wincing. He always assures me that I "look good," much like the famous scene from the movie, *Papillion*, when the emaciated, hollow-eyed Steve McQueen sticks his head out of solitary confinement for the first time and asks the other prisoners how he looks. We joke about that scene when we are at our worst, which makes it all the sweeter.

The Tin Man in my story is actually a Tin Woman, my friend Carol, who is also my Reiki practitioner. She has taught me the intrinsic value of an open heart no matter how scary and counterintuitive that may seem. Believe me, it's a process. Mine seems to keep opening and closing, but at least I am starting to prop my heart open on occasion.

Invasive lobular carcinoma is the Wicked Witch in this analogy, and I'm afraid it's going to take more than throwing a bucket of water on it to get it to go away. Cue the chemo, and radiation, and Herceptin, oh my!

My yellow brick road to breast cancer and back is paved with amazing people. And, like Dorothy on her journey, it has taken me a long time to realize they are all in my own backyard. All I can hope for is that at the end of this journey I will have more brains, more heart, and more courage.

## Satori (awakening)

Surrender like Dorothy
to that sacred place
masquerading as your own backyard.

Good witch? Bad witch?
Your true nature
wrapped in a cyclone.

The journey is paved with
conscious choices.
Be kind to blue-faced monkeys.

Inquire within.

# News from Lake Boobbegone

## Part 4

### March 2, 2014

*"Scars are tattoos with better stories."*
—Anonymous

Let me start out by recommending that no one should have surgery twice in one month; it's exhausting. From a surgical perspective, the axillary lymph node dissection on February 28th went well, but then again, they use the term "went well" a lot in the hospital. Of course, I suppose that beats the alternative.

Time will tell what story this group of lymph nodes has to reveal. I have another drain in my side, which, unfortunately, is starting to seem normal. The surgeon also inserted a chemotherapy port under my right clavicle, so I'll be good to go when the time comes. It's not as garage-door-opener noticeable or intrusive as I imagined. My bone and CT scans from last week came back clean, so now all we have to do is cut the cancer off at the pass.

I meet with the oncologist in early March to plot my chemo course and decide which drugs will be the most effective to prevent recurrence. No matter how they try to spin it, chemotherapy side effects are not for the meek. I have gained a newfound respect for all of the women who have gone before me on this roller coaster ride through hell.

My second hospital stay was only one night. Once again, I received extraordinary, compassionate care. Tom stayed with me overnight. When it comes to my well-being, he is ever vigilant and fearless.

I'm home now and propped up on the couch in time to watch the Oscars, which will pay tribute to the 75th anniversary of *The Wizard of Oz*. Coincidence? I think not.

# News from Lake Boobbegone

## Part 5

### March 6, 2014

*"You never know how strong you are until being strong is the only choice you have."*
—Bob Marley

Six days have passed since the axillary lymph node dissection. This procedure seemed to kick my ass a little more than the mastectomy, if you can believe that. I guess rooting around for lymph nodes is a tad more invasive than removing a glob of fat. The surgeon took an even dozen nodes, and four were positive for cancer, which brings us to a grand total of six positive nodes (for those keeping track).

Scarecrow, Lion, and I met with the oncologist yesterday to try to plot the best course for chemo. Scores of cancer drugs are out there, so the trick is to mix the right cocktail for each patient's specific kind of cancer; cue oncologist/ mixologist.

I like my oncologist (as much as one can like an oncologist). Even though he is younger than I am, he possesses some rather endearing avuncular qualities. Soft-spoken and sincere, he's confident I can get through this. He truly seems to have my best interests at heart and actually used the c-word—*cure*. What more could a girl ask for?

I've had a lot of help researching various types of existing chemotherapy drugs, along with their insidious side effects. Suddenly, the reason I worked in the biochemistry department for five years at a medical college has become clear. As it turns out, cardiac side effects are my biggest and most legitimate concern. Fortunately, I have a healthy heart (for now) and in Cancerland, fifty-two-years old is considered young.

Long story short, I have decided to go for what I consider the deluxe treatment package, which includes 16 chemotherapy and 30 radiation treatments, with a year of Herceptin infusions thrown in because my cancer also tested positive for a protein called human epidermal growth factor 2 (HER2). Herceptin specifically targets the HER2 protein and is known to be an effective treatment. I only intend to go through this protocol once, and as it turns out, quite a few people seem to want me around for a long time to come.

I have already asked my body for forgiveness and to stick with me through this ordeal, and I wholeheartedly believe that it will. I'm reading *When Things Fall Apart—Heart Advice for Difficult Times* by Pema Chodron (an amazing American Buddhist nun), and I'm listening to a CD with incredible guided imagery for people going through chemotherapy that helps me process what my body is going through.

My treatment starts on March 17th. I'm going to try to envision chemo as a cellular clean-up crew, be grateful for the medicine and procedures that are helping me heal, and be thankful for the not-so-gentle reminder of what is really important. Oh, and cancer...you can go now.

# News from Lake Boobbegone

## Part 6

### March 19, 2014

*"Always do what you are afraid to do."*
—Ralph Waldo Emerson

So, it turns out there's an even more ominous part of the cancer center, euphemistically called the "Day Hospital" that is actually the chemotherapy infusion lab. I arrived on Monday (St. Patrick's Day) for my first treatment accompanied by my dear friend Kathy (aka Toto). Door to door, she spent six hours with me. (I know, right?)

All treatments start with blood work. The lab report must be reviewed before the carefully concocted elixir is drawn up and treatment begins. If my blood counts are too low, my body is not strong enough for treatment, and they send me home. Since cellular misconduct is what got me here in the first place, it's hard not to take these results personally.

Waiting for the results in an overcrowded room that could have passed for an airport terminal killed more than an hour, during which time Kathy and I played a couple of word games, worked on a puzzle, and drew Zentangles, which, as the name implies, is some sort of art therapy meant to lower anxiety. It actually worked more or less, not only for me, but for Kathy, too. Besides, I'll try anything with "Zen" in the title. And I admit to not always realizing that the person gracious enough to accompany me might be a little anxious as well.

I have a chemo port as part of my anatomy now. I balked at this initially (because that's what I do), but it's turned out to be a godsend. The staff can draw blood for my labs and infuse the chemo without sticking any needles in my arm. So maybe they *do* know what they're doing.

Treatment started with three big syringes of anti-nausea medication, which is another godsend. So far, I've had no such symptoms. Instead of dripping, the first chemo drug (Adriamycin) was gently pushed through the syringe by the nurse, so it went in rather quickly. The second drug (Cytoxan) had to drip in slowly (over a period of two hours), so I tried to envision steeping tea, rather than cytotoxic chemicals. It's amazing what your mind can do.

Once again, the nurses were extraordinary. I was instructed to return on the very next day at 5:00 p.m. for an incredibly expensive injection that would reawaken my loyal and vigilant white blood cells.

Fatigue hit today, just as predicted, but the way I saw it, everyone deserves an entire day in their pajamas now and again, dozing in and out while watching *Sense and Sensibility* and *Out of Africa*. That's my spin on a totally unproductive day.

I plan to get back to work, or at least show up for part

of the day, on Monday, a week after the first treatment. If all goes according to plan, my next treatment will be in two weeks. Another good friend has signed up to accompany me that day. I'm discovering that chemo is like kindergarten: sometimes you need someone to walk in with you, even after the first day.

# If You Build It...

*"If you build it, they will come."*
—Shoeless Joe Jackson, *Field of Dreams*

One of the first things I was compelled to do after my diagnosis was to construct a healing altar, although this did not start out as a deliberate act. When this impulse began, I had no clue what I was actually doing. Then I casually mentioned to my friend, Laura, that since my diagnosis I had an inexplicable desire to gather small objects that had meaning to me and put them in one place. She informed me that I was building a healing altar. I thought it more likely that the shock of the cancer diagnosis had turned me into a hoarder.

She didn't entirely rule out that possibility, but assured me that people build altars all the time for all sorts of reasons whether they knew what they were doing or not.

I looked around the house and realized that she was right. There were mini altars everywhere. She gently suggested that I put some intent behind what I was naturally inclined to do, sit back, and watch what happened.

I soon realized I desperately needed a concrete place to acknowledge my fear and transform it into hope. A bamboo trunk I had stumbled upon in a thrift shop one wintry afternoon fit the bill. I adorned it with my favorite statues of Buddha and White Tara, candles, crystals, incense, and the cross necklace my mom had given me when I graduated from kindergarten.

I admit I was a little hesitant to tell people what I was doing. The first person I trusted not to judge me was my thirteen-year-old niece, Lily. She totally understood what I was up to and why, and asked me if she could contribute something. Her precious collection of turtle charms took their place on my altar, front and center.

In the animal kingdom, turtles are thought to be the wisest of souls because of their ability to take life as it comes, accept rather than react, and stay on their natural path. In China and Japan, turtles are a symbol of longevity. I was all for that.

After Lily's extremely wise and heartfelt gift, others started to contribute. Soon my altar was covered with rose petals, beautiful crystals and stones, angels, poetry, and prayers. Sophie (my cat) and I sat in front of that altar on a daily basis, and in the end, it gave me exactly what I was searching for, a physical place to still my mind, call upon my angels, and assuage my fears.

# Practice Doesn't Mean Perfect

*"A wounded deer leaps the highest."*
—Emily Dickinson

I was fortunate enough to have had a fledgling yoga practice in place before I was diagnosed. After my surgeries and during treatment I didn't have the strength or energy to keep up with a class, so I would roll out my mat in the spare room at home, light a few candles, lie on the floor, and sob. No more downward dog or sun salutations for me. Cancer had cut my practice to the bone, and it took all of my fortitude just to lie on the floor, cry, and get back up again.

Many months passed before I was strong enough to return to my regular yoga class and realize the somatic wisdom rolling out my mat had on my recovery. I no longer think of my mat as an inanimate object; like the altar, it became a sacred place. Every time I roll it out, I claim that sacred place, which allows me to practice no matter how sick, or tired, or frightened I am at the very moment.

Acknowledging that you are wounded is incredibly difficult, but it's the first and probably the biggest step in the healing process.

Telling people (especially my parents) that I had been diagnosed with breast cancer was extremely difficult. I thought telling them I failed geometry in the 11th grade was hard. This trumped disappointment; it broke their hearts. Saying it out loud made it all too real, and I couldn't manage to without tears for a very long time. I still had hope that my scans had been misread, or I was unknowingly cast as the lead actress in a Lifetime movie entitled *Cancer for Christmas*. None of these things were true, of course, and I had to find a way to process what I was about to go through. So I did what I always do when I can't make sense of things—write.

At first it was practical things like making lists of appointments I needed to keep and cancer books I needed to read, but over time and once I calmed down, my writing became more reflective. I decided to share my experience with friends and family through e-mail, which made me more vulnerable than ever. But soon I realized that every time I clicked the send button, my heart made way for the compassion of others, which flooded my in-box on a daily basis without fail.

# News from Lake Boobbegone

## Part 7

### April 3, 2014

*"Hope is the thing with feathers."*
—Emily Dickinson

There's always hope that I'll be the one *Journal of Clinical Oncology*-worthy chemo patient whose hair doesn't fall out. Turns out I'm not one in a million, and like most women, I've spent an embarrassing amount of time agonizing over my hair and still never liking it, so I'd have thought losing it wouldn't be such a big deal. It is.

In the "Surprise…You Have Breast Cancer" binder that comes with your diagnosis and hospital tote bag, there is a mail-order wig catalogue. Wigs are one of those items you never imagine shopping for unless it's Halloween or you're trying to spice up your marriage. But, as fate would have it, I have a friend who is a wig consultant.

Robbin knows her craft and is one of the most generous women I have ever met. She came to my rescue without hesitation.

When trying on wigs, you need to take someone along who knows you well enough and for long enough to be brutally honest. Cue Beth, who has been my sidekick (or am I hers?) for over thirty years. I highly recommend taking some wine along, too. It took three consults and more than a few tears before I finally pulled the trigger on a little blonde number the wig manufacturer named Jenny.

When I informed Tom that I had picked Jenny, he pronounced her name slowly and deliberately doing his best Forrest Gump impression to date. No time to get into the characteristics Tom and Forrest share, other than they both are Vietnam veterans who know what love is. Tom thinks I will look beautiful bald, but I suspect that's nothing more than his inner Trekkie surfacing.

I am trying hard to make peace with this cancer rather than go to war with it. I was raised as a Christian by very parochial (plaid jumpers, catechisms, original sin, you get the idea) parents but have always been drawn to the all-inclusive, compassionate nature of Buddhism.

I read a post the other day by Thubten Chodron, an American Tibetan Buddhist nun, on why the monastics shave their heads. It's a symbol of cutting off confusion, hostility, and attachment (what the Buddha called the three poisonous attitudes). When the time comes, I hope I can make that connection and rid myself of at least one of those attitudes. And I sure hope Jenny likes me.

# The Conscientious Objector

*"Give Peace a Chance."*
—John Lennon

In 1971, when Richard Nixon declared war on cancer, the militant rhetoric surrounding the disease became perfectly acceptable and downright perfunctory. I suppose this is a semi-reasonable world-leader approach to a national problem. But it doesn't make a whole lot of sense to me. As a rule, I try to avoid conflict, which probably warrants its own series of therapy sessions. Growing up Lutheran bordering on Quaker meant I wasn't wired to declare war on anything, especially my own body.

When I was confronted with the cancer diagnosis, everyone assumed I would don my pink ribbon and head into treatment with guns blazing, angry, defiant, and eventually victorious. To be honest, that never even occurred to me. If I learned anything growing up with an older brother and sister it was that whomever or whatever I fought would fight back even harder and probably win. I didn't have the desire, the time, or the energy to fight the way others thought or assumed that I would.

What did make sense to me was to try to make peace with

the cancer. If ever there was a time for self-compassion, this was it. That realization didn't mean I was giving up or would forego surgery or treatment. It meant that I would make a conscious effort to soften my approach to everything I was about to experience. First and foremost, all of the militant rhetoric surrounding cancer had to go. So I took a semantic stance and officially declared myself a conscientious objector to cancer.

I was treated at the same academic medical center that I had worked in for years, so militant cancer-speak buzzed around me like shrapnel. Until it was directed at me, I really didn't pay much attention to it. As a writer, I knew how hard it can be to find the right word or combination of words. Language is an enormous gift, and the way it's used is a conscious choice.

So when I took the time to search for the words that resonated with *me*, the bulk of my fear subsided, and I was able to move forward again. I truly believe that softening and reframing the language I used around my cancer treatment and asking those around me to do the same helped me heal tremendously.

From the very beginning, I knew my time and energy would be better spent on taking responsibility for and dealing with my cancer in a kind, compassionate way rather than beating myself up for being sick, taking a combative approach, and then demanding a cure. The kindest and wisest thing my surgeon ever said to me was "you didn't do anything wrong." Those five little words absolved me of any guilt and shifted my perspective. That's really powerful stuff.

# News from Lake Boobbegone

## Part 8

### April 13, 2014

*"Some of the worst mistakes in my life were haircuts."*
—Jim Morrison

The evening before *my mother of all haircuts*, I was fortunate enough to stumble upon (if you believe in that sort of thing) and attend a healing presence meditation. The evening ended with an offering of the mantra of Medicine Buddha, the great model of healing in the Buddhist tradition, as either a blessing or a practice. I figured I'd better opt for the blessing this time around.

Having my head shaved the next day was far less traumatic than having it come out in clumps in my hand, in the shower, or on my pillow. For that very reason, I spent two anxious days trying not to move my head and avoiding the wind. Parking structures became Dyson-like wind tunnels, forcing me to run the gauntlet every time I went to work or the mall. By Saturday, it was time, and I was ready.

Deb did the honors, shaving my head with precision and grace, while Robbin waited in the wings with Jenny (my wig). Surprisingly, I shed no tears. Apparently, the meditation stuck with me long enough to let go of my remaining tresses. I didn't have to ask Beth to go with me to the salon; she just called and asked what time she should pick me up.

Beth has been my *Velveteen Rabbit* since high school. She's the real deal when it comes to friendship. She always has gum and says stuff like, "I've been telling you for years you could rock a pixie." Tom rightfully calls us Thelma and Louise whenever we hit the road together. We will definitely be going on some kind of celebratory road trip when I come out on the other side of this.

Jenny and I caused quite the stir when we returned to work the following Monday. It took some time for us to get acquainted and for me to stop feeling like I got the lead in the school play about the girl who has cancer.

At home I wore a knit hat or nothing at all. I asked Tom if my being bald freaked him out. He didn't even look up from his book and said "It's gonna take more than that."

# News from Lake Boobbegone

## Part 9

### May 7, 2014

*"If you can't fly, then run, if you can't run, then walk,*
*if you can't walk, then crawl,*
*but whatever you do, you have to keep moving forward."*
—Martin Luther King, Jr.

I have a non-competitive nature and am notoriously uncoordinated, which means sports analogies are totally lost on me. The medical profession thrives on them, however, and I must admit that my plastic surgeon was right when he pegged cancer as a marathon, not a sprint. I've hit a milestone of sorts, finishing my first round of chemo drugs on April 30th.

My sister, Laurel (aka Glinda the Good Witch), drove nearly 300 miles and abandoned her family (which includes an endearing, absent-minded husband, two teenagers, three cats, and one dog) to spend a couple of days with me. I can't help but question the depth of this sacrifice. For whatever reason, it was absolutely wonderful and unusual to have her undivided attention.

Laurel and I are complete opposites in many ways, but over the years we've learned to admire that in each other rather than let it come between us. She's always looked out for me and believed in me more than I ever could. I am grateful that she took the time to experience first-hand what I was going through. Regardless of the circumstances, it was wonderful to spend time with her.

Other than being hit by the fatigue bus and boarding the self-pity train on occasion, I have tolerated the AC part of my chemo regimen amazingly well. AC stands for Adriamycin and Cytoxin.

Catherine, my friend and co-worker, and I have renamed AC to mean Attitude and Courage. On May 14th, I move on to TH (taxol and Herceptin), which we have dubbed "Thankful and Healthy." TH comes with its own set of side effects, which are supposed to be less menacing than the AC. However, it is still a new set of drugs, and the unknown is always accompanied with some trepidation. I will be receiving the TH every week rather than every other week, so I need to wrap my head and my heart around that. This course of treatment is 12 weeks, which takes us to the end of July. So long summer, if there is such a thing in Wisconsin this year.

I am attempting to work full time through all of this. My boss and co-workers might beg to differ on that account, but they have been incredibly patient and more than understanding with what we now refer to as my chemo-induced-cognitively-challenged state. The 1980's anti-drug public service announcement, "This is Your Brain on Drugs," depicting a sizzling egg in a frying pan became the perfect metaphor for my life. The simplest tasks (remembering computer passwords, dialing the phone, finding the ladies room) challenged me. Amnesia and dyslexia don't bode well in the workplace. Fortunately, my desk job was such that no one's life hung in the balance if I misspelled a word or dialed a wrong number.

It was the fatigue that crippled me the most. There were times I was so tired I couldn't see straight. At the end of a workday, I felt like a giant baby who hadn't napped for weeks. I usually made it to the car, or on a good day, all the way home before I started to cry out of sheer exhaustion. Crying became second nature, but no matter how often I did, it always unsettled Tom. I would come in the back door, tears streaming down my face, and he would ask me yet again what was wrong. I'd look at him in utter disbelief quavering like Laura Petrie from *The Dick Van Dyke Show* and say "Oh Tom, I have cancer," as if he didn't know.

I soon learned that it took more energy *not to* cry than *to* cry and that the shower is the perfect place, especially for multitaskers. The cascading water gave me permission to let go of all the stupid things people said that only made me feel worse; the feeling that if I'd only tried harder (at what exactly isn't clear) I never would have gotten cancer in the first place; and the all-encompassing sadness I felt not only for myself but for all of the people who were in the same boat.

Tom has been steadfast in his love and care for me, but this experience is taking a toll on him as well. With the exception of going to work, he stands guard 24/7, helps me up and down the stairs when I am unsure of my footing, cooks beautiful meals I have no appetite for and barely eat, and reads aloud to me when I am too tired to keep my eyes open.

My friends have rallied beyond belief and are determined to see me though this. Turns out the Beatles were right; I will indeed get by with a little help from my friends. I relate to song lyrics much better than sports analogies. I'll ask one of the nurses to note that in my chart.

# News from Lake Boobbegone

## Part 10

### May 28, 2014

*"If you're going through hell, keep going."*
—Winston Churchill

I have transitioned to my second set of chemotherapy drugs, but not without consequence. The taxol and Herceptin delivered a lovely red rash on my face, occasional (but manageable) joint pain, a low-grade fever, and my constant cumulative companion, fatigue. Not to worry, though, because all of these side effects are considered "within the realm of what's expected," which is triage-nurse-speak for suck it up.

I have very sensitive skin to begin with, so if I had to rank the side effects, so far the rash is the most painful and annoying. My oncologist suggested I see a dermatologist. When one "ologist" doesn't know what to do, that doctor often refers you to other "ologists." The last thing I want to do is take the time to see and be billed by yet another specialist, who without fail would prescribe steroid cream, so I turned to my Ayruvedic practitioner (aka the Angel Mary) for some of her ancient wisdom and advice.

Mary suggested that I concoct a facemask of aloe vera gel and neem, followed by organic coconut oil. The mask is incredibly soothing and is taking the redness away, and the coconut oil is restoring the moisture the taxol seems to thrive on. I am amazed at my body's natural tendency to heal if allowed, and I am grateful for Mary's support.

Other so-called expected side effects of the taxol include peripheral neuropathy, along with ridging, darkening, and loosening of the finger and toe nails to the point where they might fall off. I'm not making this up. I did a little research and found that cryotherapy during the infusion of the taxol might help prevent these side effects. (Cryotherapy uses extreme cold to freeze or destroy abnormal skin cells.) Theoretically, by decreasing the blood flow to the tissues, the amount of chemotherapy that reaches the nerves in the hands and feet diminishes. I mentioned cryotherapy to my oncologist and the nurses in the infusion lab. They were aware of and open to it, but couldn't recommend it because no studies or data existed to prove it works.

Welcome to academic medicine. When you're diagnosed with cancer, one of the perks is that you eventually stop caring what other people think and start doing things in your own best interest. Bring on the cryotherapy.

While the taxol was infused over a period of two to three hours, I sat with my toes wrapped in ice packs and my fingers immersed in a tub of ice. After three taxol and Herceptin treatments, my nails are intact, and I have had no symptoms of peripheral neuropathy. Icy fingers and toes crossed that this continues.

I am continually overwhelmed by the generosity of my chemo-sitters, individuals who have taken time out of their busy lives to help me get through this:

- Kathy (aka Toto), who ate as many popsicles as I did during treatment.
- Beth, whose mantra is "anytime, anywhere" when it comes to my well-being.
- Laurel (aka Glinda), my big sister, who somehow manages to only see the good in me.
- Pam, who is the closest thing I've come to having a college roommate and who, most importantly, keeps it all in the vault without judgment.

Don't know where I'd be without these "phenomenal women" (RIP, Maya Angelou) in my life. Nine more treatments to go, but who's counting?

# News from Lake Boobbegone

## Part 11

### June 18, 2014

*"Pain is certain, suffering is optional."*
—Buddha

I'm typing this at 4:30 a.m., as I contemplate the irony of being too tired to sleep. My last four infusion-filled hours were spent in the company of Kim, my newest volunteer chemo-sitter, who is also a co-worker and friend. She could have cheered up Stalin. I sat in my recliner cocooned in the fleece peace blanket my niece Lily made for me, eating a cherry Popsicle, which has become my signature chemo snack of choice, while Kim tuned in the spa music channel on her iPad.

I finished number 10 of the 16 chemotherapy treatments I signed on for and am beginning to see a flicker of light at the end of the tunnel. In terms of side effects, I do believe I've been luckier than most in tolerating the treatment. I am especially grateful that I've managed to maintain my sense of humor through all of this, while keeping public meltdowns to a minimum. It has also occurred to me that my game face may be glossing over how difficult this process really is.

Truth be told, having cancer and trying to be brave about it is physically, mentally, emotionally, and spiritually exhausting. People (especially Tom) who have the pleasure of interacting with me on a daily basis understand it, as do the multitude of patients in the infusion lab who are in various stages of cancer and treatment themselves. Cancer is commonplace, and if you don't have it yourself, chances are you know someone who does. That doesn't make it any easier when it happens to you. Misery does *not* love company in this case. It compounds the collective sadness.

As I write this, I'm at my kitchen table with an aloe and neem facemask on in an attempt to thwart the burning taxol face rash that presents itself like clockwork the day after treatment. I'll shower soon, strategically avoiding the mirror or even looking down for too long at what remains of my body. Next, I'll try to find clothes that don't draw attention to how out of balance I look and feel. Then I'll attempt to draw on eyebrows that don't make me look like Joan Crawford. And finally, I'll say good morning to my wig Jenny and ask her to help me get through one more day.

# News from Lake Boobbegone

## Part 12

### August 1, 2014

*"Perhaps all of the dragons of our lives are princesses who are only waiting to see us once beautiful and brave."*
—Rainer Maria Rilke

When you're thrown into the deep end without a warning, it's difficult to ever imagine surfacing, especially when you can't swim. The last of my 16 chemotherapy treatments was infused on July 30th, two days ago, and it finally feels like I'm coming up for air.

Kathy (Toto), who accompanied me for the first treatment, along with a few other treatments in between, was with me for the last. Somehow, that seemed fitting. She arrived with the dark-chocolate-covered-raisins I asked for, a vintage version of the game Password she dug out of her basement, and roses. I wore my favorite red patent leather Mary Jane's, as close as I could get to ruby slippers.

That morning, the lab was so busy it had a two-hour waiting

time. How had so many people managed to get themselves into the same situation I had, I wondered? That aside, I once again had an extremely competent and compassionate nurse. Other staff recognized me and realized that it was my last treatment, perhaps because I kept blurting it out like a two-year-old to anyone and everyone who glanced in my direction.

Well wishes and hugs appropriately marked this milestone in my treatment. It's not like I wouldn't be back, though. I have an entire year of Herceptin infusions on my to-do list. However, those treatments are on what they call the fast track, and are administered once every three weeks rather than every week. They take only 30 minutes, which seems like a drive-through window compared to the four-hour treatments I have grown accustomed to. So basically, it's gravy. I guess everything is relative.

At the end of the treatment, they handed me a certificate of achievement for "uncommon valor, courage, and good humor" through chemotherapy. It couldn't have gotten any more Wizard of Oz-ish than that. Attributes like valor and courage had been no doubt buried deep inside me all along, but like my breath, were given the opportunity to surface under these extraordinary circumstances. I still have a long road ahead of me with two reconstructive procedures and six weeks of daily radiation therapy on the horizon. Making it through 16 chemotherapy treatments was significant. At least it was for me.

When it comes to cancer, the word "journey" doesn't sit well with me, mostly because it is so overused, and at least in my mind, cliché. Semantically, my experience seems more like a *trip*, which aptly includes and describes my altered state. I'm confident that the drugs will serve their purpose, take only what they need and go. I'm confident that my body will forgive me, and my immune system will take this opportunity to rebuild itself. I have come to realize that the times when life seems too much to bear, and I am at my weariest is also when I'm doing the best life work. Perhaps the most important work.

This whole cancer trip is my opportunity, which is suddenly so radiant and suddenly so clear.

# Permission Slip

*"The wound is the place where light enters you."*
—Rumi

Cancer gave me the permission slip I needed to truly put myself first. Admittedly, scores of people might beg to differ, perhaps claiming that I've been doing this my entire life. In fact, I've often been labeled self-centered for many of the choices I've made. I suppose the biggest decision was not marrying the guy I dated for over three years. He was the guy with the steady job, good health insurance, and an inexplicable desire to take care of me. Rather than comfort me, it made me feel as if I had a plastic bag over my head.

Instead, I opted out of that relationship and chose Tom, a freelance artist I'd known for only five months before moving in with him and four more months before marrying him. Somehow, I'd found the courage to follow my own heart, which had been labeled selfish or stupid, usually by those who didn't have the courage to do the same.

When Tom and I made the conscious decision not to have children, nearly everyone in our lives viewed that as the ultimate act of selfishness. Interestingly enough, Tom and I are both *that dreaded unplanned last child* in our families whose presence was merely tolerated. We were often allowed more freedom than our older siblings simply because our parents had run out of disciplinary steam. We both know first-hand how awkward and downright painful it is to be at a party you weren't invited to that turns out to be your own life.

In my case, I was cast as the third interloper into an idyllic family of one girl and one boy. Rest assured, this is not something I am conjuring up to get attention. I got the story directly from my mother. In fact, while she was pregnant with me and throughout her life, my mother told the story about how she sat down at the kitchen table and cried for weeks on end when she found out she was expecting another baby.

It's my belief that disrupting the perfect family paradigm was something I sensed *in utero*. How dare I upset the apple cart, tip the scales, and outnumber the adults in the household forevermore? With three kids under the age of five, my mother was convinced that she would never get out from under the yoke of motherhood; as a result, I unconsciously spent my entire life trying to validate my existence by pleasing not only my parents but everyone else as well. This made me woefully obedient, quiet as a mouse (not coincidentally my childhood nickname), excruciatingly accommodating, and on a physical level, I was pale, tired, and nearly invisible. I also attended twelve years of parochial school, which only added fuel to the fire.

During the last ten years of my mother's life, helping her dress after yet another doctor's appointment had become routine. One day when I leaned over to tie her shoes, she admitted once again to the top of my head that she never wanted me, but now she didn't know what she'd do without me. Before I was finished with tying her shoes, she put me into the "God's Plan" column of her life, just like she did everything else she couldn't figure out, rationalize, or explain. It was one of the few times that she actually expressed her true feelings to me. I was all for that, but just not at my expense. It seems it doesn't work that way, however. The truth is the truth and more often than not it hurts.

Ironically, I was the one of her three children who spent the most time with her, listened to her stories, took her to the doctor, and massaged whatever part of her body that hurt the most. In the end, I checked her into hospice care, which gave her the final permission slip she needed to let go. I don't believe my mother deliberately set out to hurt me, but like all exhausted and fallible mothers, she did.

As pathetically desperate and childish as it sounds, I thought, if anything, the cancer would finally be my ticket to the love and attention I thought I'd been denied. When I was diagnosed, Mom was in her late eighties and suffering from a laundry list of health problems. Near the end, it included the rapid onset of dementia. While feeding her lunch one day, she looked directly at me and asked me my name.

When I said, "I'm Carolyn," she smiled slightly and said that would be easy to remember because she had a daughter with the same name. After a few more bites, she smiled again and told me that I was the nicest girl who worked at the nursing home.

That's the day I forgave her for being human and started to heal.

# News from Lake Boobbegone

## Part 13

### August 30, 2014

*"The best way out is always through."*
—Robert Frost

It felt like I'd won some sort of surgical lottery when the hospital called to reschedule my first reconstructive procedure. Instead of waiting until 3:15 p.m., I was rescheduled to 8:30 a.m. on Friday, so barring any natural disasters it was likely they'd be running on time, even though hospital time does stand freakishly still once they slap an ID bracelet on you.

I'm a month out from my last chemo treatment, and since my energy level is on the upswing, they figured it was time to throw another procedure at me. When I had the mastectomy way back in February, something called an *expander* was put in to gently stretch my skin and hold space for the breast implant. Every other week, I would visit the plastic surgery clinic where they would inject saline into the expander until it got to a size that I was comfortable with that particular day. This was done in what the surgeon considered small, tolerable increments. I'm not so sure I'd agree.

The skin on my chest was literally being stretched, and no matter how slowly, it hurt like hell. I quickly learned to take Tylenol before each weekly appointment in an attempt to cut some of the discomfort off at the pass. As the expander did as intended and expanded, it took on the characteristics of an upside down Tupperware bowl crazy glued to my chest by a kindergartner. The expander made me feel plastic, inanimate, and phony. I won't go as far as to say I had been looking forward to yesterday's surgery, but it was a relief to finally swap out the immobile expander for the more malleable, user-friendly implant.

Tom was there to hold my hand, as he'd done on countless occasions and to hold my purse, which he only does in emergency situations; this must have qualified. The plastic surgeon came by with his Sharpie to mark me up even before I had a chance to change into my huge paper gown; time-wise I viewed this as a good sign.

The anesthesiologist came in soon after to explain what type of sedation I would be receiving. I wasn't put under general anesthesia. That might not sound like a good thing but actually it was, as the recovery time is much faster. They let me wear my lucky hat with the yin and the yang symbol on it into the operating room; yet another good sign.

Once I was prepped and warned about all of the things that could go horribly awry during surgery, they wheeled me into the blindingly lit operating room that was so cold it felt like I'd been cast as an extra in the movie *Ice Station Zebra*. A team of masked automatons restrained me in an alien abduction kind of way. Apparently, I've watched way too many *X-Files* episodes.

Since I wasn't completely anesthetized, I could hear the staff talking amongst themselves throughout the procedure about mundane things, like Labor Day weekend plans and getting their kids ready to go back to school. They might have been standing around a water cooler in a scene from *Mad Men*. I found that oddly comforting. Of course, the drugs had kicked in a major way by that time, so no doubt I would have found just about anything oddly comforting, including the fictionalized advertising executive Don Draper operating on me.

The procedure itself only took an hour. Total time spent from check-in to check-out was five hours. Their parting gift, along with the silicone gel implant of course, was a surgical bra. It's as pretty as it sounds, and itchy and scratchy to boot. I had to wear it 24/7 for six weeks or until the incision healed.

On the way home, Tom stopped to pick up my pain medication along with a self-prescribed pint of tiramisu gelato. Both seemed to help tremendously. The holiday weekend would be spent dozing in and out, reading, feeling sorry for myself, and watching *Casablanca* and *Annie Hall* for the umpteenth time.

Next stop—radiation road.

# News from Lake Boobbegone

## Part 14

### September 28, 2014

*"Forgive yourself for not being at peace. The moment you completely accept your non-peace, your non-peace is transmuted into peace. This is the miracle of surrender."*
—Eckhart Tolle

My next course of treatment was underway. Specifically, six weeks of daily radiation therapy. Word on the street is that compared to chemotherapy, radiation therapy is a cakewalk. Not so much in my case. At times, I found it more challenging than chemotherapy. Before treatment could begin, two 45-minute simulations were required that included a CT scan, multiple x-rays, the application of miniscule tattoos, and the painstakingly meticulous lining up of the discombobulating machines. So, basically, target practice.

It is paramount that I'm in the exact same position each time a dose of radiation is given, which I totally understand.

What I hadn't understood ahead of time is that I would be put in restraints in order to achieve this.

Here's where I, and I imagine countless others, have issues. Positioning for treatment requires that I lie on my back on a narrow metal morgue-like table with my arms overhead crucifixion-style. A mold was made of my left arm to ensure its exact placement each and every time. Then came the chinstrap—you read that correctly—chinstrap, made of a mesh-like material, molded to my chin, and then fastened securely (insert ominous metal clicking sounds) to the table on both sides of my head. Because it was the only thing that could move, my mind raced from Hannibal Lecter in *Silence of the Lambs*, to Christ on the cross, to Sylvia Plath in *The Bell Jar*. I suddenly remembered being five years old and having my tonsils out. The nurses had tied me in bed at night so I wouldn't fall out when they weren't watching me. It was the only time I cried, and I was about to again.

Next came what sounded to me like cheap duct tape being pulled off the roll. The radiation technicians used this tape on my right breast to make sure that it was out of the treatment field. As far as I could tell, gravity had taken care of that, and it was closer to my right armpit than the treatment field, but down it went securely taped to the metal table. There was no negotiating at this point. In some feeble attempt to protect them, tape went over all of the scars on my left "breast" and under my arm as well. The radiation techs assured me that this was all normal procedure. I set them straight about any of this being normal.

The treatments, about 20 minutes each, go much faster than the simulations. The radiation techs double-team me, so it takes about five minutes to restrain and about15 minutes for the actual intermittent blasts of radiation, at which point they all head for the hills.

During these weeks of radiation, my anxiety level and vulnerable state sent me running to my acupuncturist in search of my calming meridian. After my regular session with her, she sent me home with two very tiny needles inserted in the calming points of both of my ears. I left the needles in for the second simulation and planned to go back for more.

I have chosen a mantra: *I am surrounded by light*. I hope this helps to soothe my monkey mind, which in turn will allow me to breathe a little bit deeper than I did the time before.

Inching along in traffic on my way home from my second 45-minute simulation, I tried desperately to figure out how I was going to get through the next six weeks of this treatment. I looked up, as one often instinctively does at times like these, and saw what looked to me like the Wicked Witch's smoke-filled message sprawled across a bright blue sky: *Surrender Dorothy*.

Suddenly I realized that all I needed to do was to *allow* what was happening and keep moving through it, rather than trying to figure a way around it or out of it entirely. Buddhism 101.

This realization didn't mean I would like it any better, or guarantee it would be any easier, or that by some miracle I'd stop whining; it simply meant that in time—and like Dorothy—I will land on the other side of this, just as I had with the surgeries and the chemotherapy. With all that I've gone through, you would think I'd have learned this by now. Sometimes, it takes me awhile.

And then I smiled, because I remembered that usually

it's the Wicked Witches in your life that teach you the most valuable lessons.

# News from Lake Boobbegone

## Part 15

### October 21, 2014

*"Turn your wounds into wisdom."*
—Oprah Winfrey

I was exactly halfway through my radiation therapy: 15 treatments behind me, 15 more to go when the treatments started to become "easier" because I was no longer required to wear the chinstrap. I convinced my radiation oncologist that if I'd learned anything in parochial school it was how to sit perfectly still for inordinate periods of time. She agreed. However, she then exchanged the chinstrap for a mesh breastplate that's supposed to help distribute the radiation more precisely. Unlike the chinstrap, which was confining and uncomfortable, I found the breastplate comforting. The first time I donned it, I had visions of Joan of Arc. Seriously.

So far, my skin was holding up fairly well. To thwart the radiation burn, I used an organic calendula cream my Reiki practitioner made, rather than the chemical-laden cream the nurses gave me. I'm counting on calendula and St. Joan to save my skin. I slathered the cream on immediately after my treatment and then again at night before I went to bed.

Daily treatments were making me weepy and weary. Tom handled my meltdowns with compassion and open arms. It occurred to me that the "in sickness" clause in our wedding vows was being put to the test—and he was passing with flying colors.

When I hit a low point, the Universe always puts something in my path to remind me that I am not alone in this struggle. Last week the annual fund raising campaign for UPAF (United Performing Arts Fund) was in full swing, which meant musicians were scattered throughout the medical complex campus. I tended to feel the most sorry for myself while walking over to the clinic for my daily treatments. That's why when I heard "Over the Rainbow" in the distance being strummed on a lone banjo; I had to blink back my tears.

Crossing paths with that musician who chose to play that song at that particular moment in time was no coincidence. The day before I was sitting in the waiting room with a woman I saw almost every day. Dressed like fraternal twins in the greatest fashion equalizer known to man, the blue hospital gown, we gave each other the same weak smile and knowing nod, as we anxiously waited for our names to be called.

Finally, I broke the ice and introduced myself. When she said her name was Faith, I put my hand to my heart in gratitude because finding faith was exactly what I had prayed for on the way over to my appointment. Who knew faith had been with me all along mysteriously disguised as another cancer patient?

Jenny and I remained constant companions. Tom still has more hair than I do, and for now I will let him have his moment in the sun. Surprisingly, my hair is growing back dark and gray. I even managed to forget that I'm not a natural blonde. Time will tell if I have the courage to let nature take its course. This year, my Halloween costume possibilities include Sinead O'Conner, a member of the Manson family, or GI Jane.

# News from Lake Boobbegone

## Part 16

### November 27, 2014, Thanksgiving Day

*"I believe illness has led me to a life of gratitude."*
—Rebecca Wells

So, these are the top ten things I've had to let go of this year: (1) my left breast, (2) 15 lymph nodes, (3) all of my hair, (4) my immune system, (5) my idea of beauty, (6) the illusion of control, (7) cocktails, (8) a plethora of tears, (9) a few extra pounds, and (10) wondering why me.

My last radiation treatment, or as I liked to euphemistically call it, "light therapy," took place on November 10th. But even weeks after the treatment ended, radiation had left me looking and feeling like I'd been microwaved on high for far too long. Next to the mother of all sunburns, the emotional fatigue of daily treatments was probably the worst of it. I had been living "cancerously" for nearly a year now, and it had taken all of my resolve. Unlike chemo, I had to face radiation therapy on my own. No one could go with me, hold my hand, or sit by my side and distract me from these treatments. I had to dig deep and find even more strength I wasn't sure I could muster.

The "mean wells," my term for people who say dumb stuff unintentionally, keep reminding me how great things will be once I get back to normal. I don't see how that is even remotely possible. I am missing a body part, have been infused with drugs potent enough to damage my heart and make my hair fall out, have been microwaved on high for 30 consecutive days, and as an added bonus have been chemically catapulted into menopause. And those are just the physical ramifications. Mix in equal parts anxiety, fear, and sadness, and the cancer train I've been on misses all the normal stops. What a disappointment and missed opportunity it would be if, after all of this, I turned out to be the exact same person I was before I was diagnosed.

I can't quite go as far as to say that I am grateful I was diagnosed with breast cancer, but I *can* say that I am grateful for all of the realizations that have resulted because of it. I was given the opportunity to tap into a reservoir of courage I didn't even know existed. I witnessed people at their best as they surrounded me with their clinical, surgical, and scientific expertise, genuine concern, humor, compassion, energy, and love. The word friendship took on a whole new meaning with each chemo sitter who took time out of her busy life to sit with me for hours on end. And I found out that my marriage was indeed for better or worse.

This Thanksgiving would be like no other because I finally understood the importance and power of gratitude. I had gained far more than I had lost this year and for that I was extremely grateful.

# News from Lake Boobbegone

## Part 17

### January 4, 2015

*"No matter how hard the past,*
*you can always begin again."*
—Buddha

The New Year is a natural time for reflection. When I thought back on everything I experienced in 2014, I'm easily overwhelmed by the enormity of it all. First, there was the shock, utter disbelief, and sadness over the diagnosis itself. Surely there must have been some mistake. Breast cancer happens to the neighbor lady, a coworker, or the checker at the grocery store, not to me. The Universe hurled me to boldly go where statistically—and sadly—one in eight women have gone before.

Next in line were the impossible surgical decisions that had to be made quickly, along with the looming fear of the latest cancer treatments; somehow, after years of research and new discoveries they still seem medieval. Everyone kept assuring me that I would get through it, but when pressed for an answer as to how, they all came up empty. Everyone, that is, except for my yoga teacher, Judy, who, ever since I set foot and heart into her class many years ago, had been gently reminding me over and over again to *live in the moment*. It's not as easy as it sounds.

I was familiar with the Alcoholics Anonymous philosophy of living one day at a time, and the Doobie Brothers suggesting we live "minute by minute," but I soon realized that I was in a situation where that wasn't even slow enough. Here's where Judy (and Sting) come in with *Every Breath You Take*.

It took every ounce of energy I had to simply inhale and exhale as they wheeled me into the operating room (twice), as I watched the chemotherapy drugs drip from the IV bag into my bloodstream for the very first time, and as they restrained me for radiation therapy as if I had been committed to an asylum. Judy had taught me how to breathe. It isn't always a given or the spontaneous miracle we expect. I waded into Cancerland with this valuable tool, and it served me beyond measure.

Since this whole cancer thing, I've gotten really good at recognizing and interpreting signs from the Universe. It's one of the perks. Tom often wakes me up by whispering sweet and/or creepy things in my ear. But this morning when I distinctly heard the two words "begin again" and opened my eyes, he was nowhere to be found. This sign was a little on the obvious side, even for me.

I'm not one for making New Year's resolutions, but those two words got me thinking about how much time I've spent resisting the idea of starting over. I've burned brownies, failed tests, been fired from jobs, put the wrong color clothes together in the washing machine, made a mess of relationships, and dinged the car badly. But the beauty in all of that, once the guilt and humiliation passed is that I had the opportunity to begin again. What more could a girl ask for?

As of the New Year, Jenny, my wig and constant companion, and I have parted ways. Talk about starting over. My hair is growing back rather dark and mostly gray, and for now I am okay with that. Whether they mean it or not, everyone says it looks great, and I am okay with that too. I have Herceptin infusions every three weeks until May, and an appointment with the plastic surgeon again in January to discuss more reconstruction options. But most importantly, I went back to my yoga class, so I was starting over in that regard as well. And for the first time ever, I am more than okay with that.

# News from Lake Boobbegone

## Part 18

### April 6, 2015

*"Write hard and clear about what hurts."*
—Ernest Hemingway

Dearest Lake Boobbegone Readers:

It's been months since my last missive, and if that has caused any concern, I apologize. No news is usually good news in Cancerland. I'm nearing the end of my treatment, with only two more Herceptin infusions to go and a reconstructive procedure on the horizon. The insurance company gods are deciding my fate in that regard.

More side effects are beginning to surface, including cataracts resulting from the steroid drugs and hypothyroidism aggravated by the radiation therapy, which probably explains why I wear mittens to bed. These side effects, while manageable, are nonetheless disheartening. For now, vision issues can be corrected with a new prescription for glasses and contact lenses. I plan to work with my naturopath, acupuncturist, and Reiki practitioner to restore my natural thyroid function using supplements, diet, and energy work. My body deserves the opportunity to rally naturally before hopping on the Synthroid train. So far, no cardiac side effects have surfaced, and for that I'm grateful.

My biggest challenge from now on will be finding a way to surrender my fear and make peace with the uncertainty ahead, both in terms of future side effects, and in adjusting to the word no cancer patient ever wants to hear, recurrence. *How* I choose to react to whatever comes my way is what is most important. I've had plenty of "poor me" moments, but I also realize how fortunate I've been and how many others are struggling with the same issues. I can only hope that others facing this disease have the resources and incredible support that I've been offered and have received.

I'm back to my fledgling massage therapy practice, with the added hope of getting further education in oncology massage. I have experienced first-hand (no pun intended) the need for a nurturing touch rather than just a surgical or clinical one, especially at times like these. In terms of my practice, it will be interesting to see where my cancer experience takes me.

Tom is forever by my side accompanying me on long walks and cooking me nutritious meals. I am planning a girls' weekend in April and time away with my sister in July. Life seems to be taking on a healthy new rhythm.

I want to thank each of you for sticking with me through the most challenging year of my life to date. Everyone brought something different to the table at exactly the right moment; encouragement, compassion, medical advice, wigs, humor, food, cards, flowers, books, prayers, energy, and most importantly, love. Writing and sharing these updates has helped me heal tremendously.

# News from Lake Boobbegone

## Part 19

### July 10, 2015

*"Sometimes good things fall apart*
*so better things can fall together."*
—Marilyn Monroe

I believe everything happens for a reason. That said, I must admit cancer is a tough one. Since my diagnosis last year, four friends have either been newly diagnosed or had recurrences, and one passed away.

I still wonder what made my cells so angry and go terribly awry. Could it really have been the white bread and processed cheese I ate as a kid? Did I simply drink one too many glasses of chardonnay or microwave too much stuff in plastic containers before I knew better? Did my experiences and the stress of everyday life send my DNA into a tailspin? Or is this some big cosmic plan to make me a better person?

I don't know if I'm a better person, but I certainly am a different one. There are still the obvious physical changes that have taken some getting used to. But they all seem relatively minor, especially when compared to the way I now look at the world and the gratitude I have for every single day—even if it's a bad one.

I have one more surgical procedure scheduled on August 14th. I am hopeful enough to believe that I'll be done after that. No doubt the lessons of my cancer experience will keep surfacing whether or not I am in treatment. I will try to keep my heart as wide open as I possibly can to receive them.

I lost a huge part of my heart when my mom decided to let go of this life on June 24th. I was around for fifty-two of her eighty-eight years. What an astonishing gift. As clichéd as it might sound, I truly believe that she is in a better place, free from all of the pain and suffering she endured, especially near the end of her life.

Hug your mom every chance you get. She gave you your life, no matter how hard or crummy you might think it is on any given day. Mother-daughter relationships are, at their best, complex and evolve over time. Ours was no exception. As the dementia crept in and our roles reversed, it was the first time I realized how much love a mother has for her child. Having no children of my own left me clueless in that regard. When I had to start tying her shoes, clipping her fingernails, and helping her eat, I got a glimpse into the exhausting, under-appreciated, selfless act of motherhood. As tiring and sad as it was to watch her regress, I am grateful that I had the opportunity to truly understand the daily sacrifices she made for our family that simply fell under the auspices of being called *mom*.

My next stop before reconstructive surgery is a trip to the Lavender Festival on Washington Island in Door County in

Northeast Wisconsin. What better tonic than lavender fields and time away with my dear sister?

# News from Lake Boobbegone

## Part 20

### August 17, 2015

*"Breathe-in experience, breathe-out poetry."*
—Muriel Rukeyser

August 14th marked my final reconstructive procedure, the purpose of which was to shore up my right breast to match the implant. Since my breasts never matched before, I was skeptical from the get go, imagining this quite the surgical feat. I had considered skipping this last procedure altogether, but my plastic surgery team assured me that it would be worth the time and effort. Plus, it was the last part of the cancer package they sold me back in February of 2014. One more hoop.

Walking around lopsided for a year and a half had taken a physical and emotional toll. I always felt like I was hiding under my old lady office sweater or a strategically placed (albeit fashionable) scarf. Still, correcting the situation meant another major surgery in less than two years. After the mastectomy, lymph node dissection, chemotherapy, radiation therapy, and losing my mom, I admittedly went into this surgery on the weaker end of the spectrum.

How much can a body endure? Turns out, quite a lot.

Tom was with me, of course, and seemed even more relieved than I was that this was the last stop on the cancer train. When the anesthesiologist asked me to take in deep yoga breaths, I surrendered my fear and literally placed myself in the surgical team's hands. And in what seemed like the blink of an eye they made me wake up, throw up, and get up. Four not-so-tiny incisions and a chemo port scar repair/do over later, the three-hour outpatient procedure was complete. They practically wheeled me from the operating room to my car.

Home I was, wrapped tighter than an anorexic mummy in a surgical bra that was then topped off with an enormous ace bandage. Plus, a drain in my side oozed goo. The weekend was spent trying to breathe, finding a comfortable position, itching, scratching, wincing, and stripping the drain. By Saturday, I downgraded myself from oxycodone to an occasional extra strength Tylenol and a pint of Cherry Garcia ice cream.

On Monday I had a follow up appointment with the plastic surgeon, and the drain was removed. What a relief. Now there's just a gaping hole. The plastic surgery team said I looked fabulous, which immediately had me questioning their definition of *fabulous*. It was hard not to feel like I was back on team Frankenstein.

When I'm out of sorts, I read poetry. Last night I reached for my tried and true volume of Emily Dickinson's poems and opened it at random.

*Beauty—be not caused—it is*
*Chase it, and it ceases*
*Chase it not, and it abides*

Just for the record, I have officially switched to team Dickinson.

*Beauty abides.*

# Afterword

*"All I know to do is to light the candle that has been given to me."*
—Fred Rogers a.k.a. Mister Rogers

When you're living with the uncertainty of recurrence, it's difficult to know when, where, or how to end a cancer memoir. For all intents and purposes, my oncologist has put me in the cured column, which is where I intend to stay in order to enjoy what seems like the proverbial happy ending. Some days, though, it's not so obvious.

As I changed into the all too familiar blue hospital gown for a recent mammogram, my heart began to race. Clearly, I was experiencing some low level post-traumatic stress from my ordeal. I have an appointment every four months, flip-flopping between my oncologist and radiation oncologist. Soon the appointments will spread out to every six months, and eventually only once a year. To thwart recurrence, I take tamoxifen daily, which blocks the female hormone estrogen that "feed" certain types of breast cancer. But I also know that taking tamoxifen may also increase my risk of uterine cancer, stroke, or blood clots in my lungs. It's a tradeoff many women face. I also struggle with my body image and the reconstructive procedures that seemed too good to be true and indeed were.

The holistic practitioners and practices I relied on during treatment remain just as necessary and important as my allopathic follow up appointments. I continue to practice yoga and meditate. I see my naturopath, my acupuncturist, my Reiki practitioner, and most recently, a holistic practitioner that helps post-cancer patients thrive in the aftermath of treatment and move on from their experience.

Navigating through breast cancer has challenged me like nothing else in my life, but in the end, it allowed me to examine and soften my own heart, realize my own self-worth, and most importantly turn what seemed like never-ending darkness into light.

# Recommended Reading


Kamm, Laura Alden: *Intuitive Wellness: Using Your Body's Inner Wisdom to Heal*

Chodron, Pema: *When Things Fall Apart: Heart Advice for Difficult Times*

Chodron, Pema: *Living Beautifully with Uncertainty and Change*

Dickinson, Emily: *The Complete Poems of Emily Dickinson*

Fortson, Leigh: *Embrace, Release, Heal: An Empowering Guide to Talking About, Thinking About, and Treating Cancer*

Lifshitz, Leatrice H. (Editor): *Her Soul Beneath the Bone: Women's Poetry on Breast Cancer*

Linn, Denise: *Altars: Bringing Sacred Shrines into Your Everyday Life*

Norton, Meredith: *Lopsided: How Having Breast Cancer Can Be Very Distracting*

*News from Lake Boobbegone*

Rodgers, Joni: *Bald in the Land of Big Hair*

Silver, Tosha: *Outrageous Openness—Letting the Divine Take the Lead*

# Recommended Listening

Anugama: "Healing"

Deuter: "Spiritual Healing"

Jobst, Benjamin: "Seven Metals—Singing Bowls of Tibet"

Malkin, Gary with Hemi-Sync: "The Music of Graceful Passages"

Naparstek, Belleruth: "Meditation to Help You with Chemotherapy" (Health Journeys) Audio CD, January 1, 1991

Naparstek, Belleruth: "Meditation to Help You with Radiation Therapy" (Health Journeys) Audio CD, January 1, 1999

Sounds True Staff/Various Artists: "Cancer as a Turning Point: From Surviving to Thriving," Volume 1 and 2

Tolle, Eckhart: "Music to Quiet the Mind"

**If you enjoyed News from Lake Boobbegone, you may enjoy this title from Written Dreams Publishing.**

# Shaking the Family Tree

*A Journey from Addiction to Recovery*

## Dallas H.

**Spring 2017 Release**

***There was a boogie man in the closet and its name was alcoholism.***

***Shaking the Family Tree*** is an anonymous personal memoir of a recovering alcoholic interlaced with poetic offerings of the ramifications of the disease of alcoholism. Dallas's story is one of coming to terms with what has become her family's unfortunate legacy. Traced back for four generations, it continues to reveal itself in her family.

In her memoir, Dallas explains her battle with co-dependency, and the genetic predisposition for alcoholism being the single thread that ties it all together of what made her life a living hell. Dallas didn't give up. Although she wanted to kick the habit, it wasn't easy. Dallas shares how she conquered her biggest demons and became a survivor of alcoholism.

# Acknowledgements

Never ending gratitude to the medical/surgical staff, holistic practitioners, family, and friends, who not only stood by me but held me up through this experience.

Catherine Schulls for coming up with the title and letting me use it.

Virginia McCullough for her kindness, editorial expertise, and reassurance this project was worthwhile.

Brittiany Koren for her publishing acumen and encouragement to tell the truth.

Bob Kliegman for reminding me and demonstrating on a daily basis that the reason we're all here is to help each other.

## About the Author

Carolyn Redman has been writing poetry and short stories since junior high school, where she was erroneously labeled by her guidance counselor as having the wrong kind of imagination. She persevered, earning a BA (cum laude) from Mount Mary University in English/Professional Writing, while working full time as an editorial assistant at an academic medical institution. She is a WI state licensed, board certified massage therapist who believes strongly in integrative medicine and the mind body connection. She was born and raised in Milwaukee, WI where she lives with her artist husband Tom and their cat Sophie. ***News from Lake Boobbegone*** is her first published work.